Hours with the Masters

Volume 2 (Transitional)

Selected graded classics for Piano including fingering, phrasing, interpretative notes, metronome rates etc., by Dorothy Bradley.

Stunden mit den Meistern

Band 2 (Übergangsstufe)

Klassische und neuzeitliche Stücke für Klavier nach Schwierigkeitsgraden ausgewählt, mit Fingersatz, Phrasierungs-, Tempo- und Ausdrucksangaben versehen von Dorothy Bradley.

Avec les Maîtres du Piano

Volume 2 (Degré transitoire)

Des oeuvres classiques choisies par ordre de difficulté. Doigtés, phrasés, notes d'interprétation, mouvements métronomiques etc., par Dorothy Bradley.

Bosworth

2

Étude en Do

Un bon élan rythmique est nécessaire. Ne faites aucune rupture entre les accords brisés que les mains se partagent. Faites usage d'une frappe percutante pour les accords *sf* avec une frappe de doigts ferme et de l'énergie dans l'avant-bras.

Study in C

Good rhythmic impetus is needed. Do not make any breaks between the broken chords shared by the hands. Use a percussive touch for the *sf* chords with firm fingers and forearm energy touch.

Studie in C-dur

Dieses Stück erfordert einen guten rhythmischen Antrieb. Die von beiden Händen gespielten gebrochenen Akkorde dürfen keine Unterbrechung erfahren. Spiele die sf-Akkorde mit fester Fingerhaltung und einem vom Unterarm herkommenden schlagzeugartigen, energischen Anschlag.

Allegro vivace ♩ = 132

Heller, Op. 125, No. 3

4

Étude en Fa

Fluidité des doigts, vigueur rythmique et bonnes variations de sonorité sont nécessaires. Remarquez que l'air est donné par le cinquième doigt ou le pouce de la main, jusqu'aux mesures 13 à 16, où, en soutenant les notes pointées, nous obtenons un effet de rythme croisé qui, toutefois, ne doit pas déranger les battements réguliers. Un accent sur les notes pointées produit l'effet qui convient.

Study in F

Finger fluency, rhythmic vigour and good tone variants are needed. Observe that the tune lies at the fifth finger or thumb side of the hand, until bars 13 to 16 where, by sustaining the dotted notes we get an effect of cross-rhythm which, however, must not disturb the regular beats. An accent on the dotted notes makes the right effect.

Studie in F-dur

Für diese Studie sind Fingergeläufigkeit, kraftvoller Rhythmus und gute Tonmodulationen notwendig. Beachte, dass der fingertechnische Schwerpunkt beim Spielen der Melodiestimme einmal auf der Seite des 5. Fingers, das andere Mal auf der Daumenseite liegt. In den Takten 13-16 unterbrechen die ausgehaltenen punktierten Noten den gleichmässigen Rhythmus. Das Metrum muss jedoch trotzdem klar zu erkennen sein. Mit dem Akzent auf der punktierten Note wird die angestrebte Wirkung erreicht.

Molto vivo ♩ = 144

Heller, Op. 47, No. 1

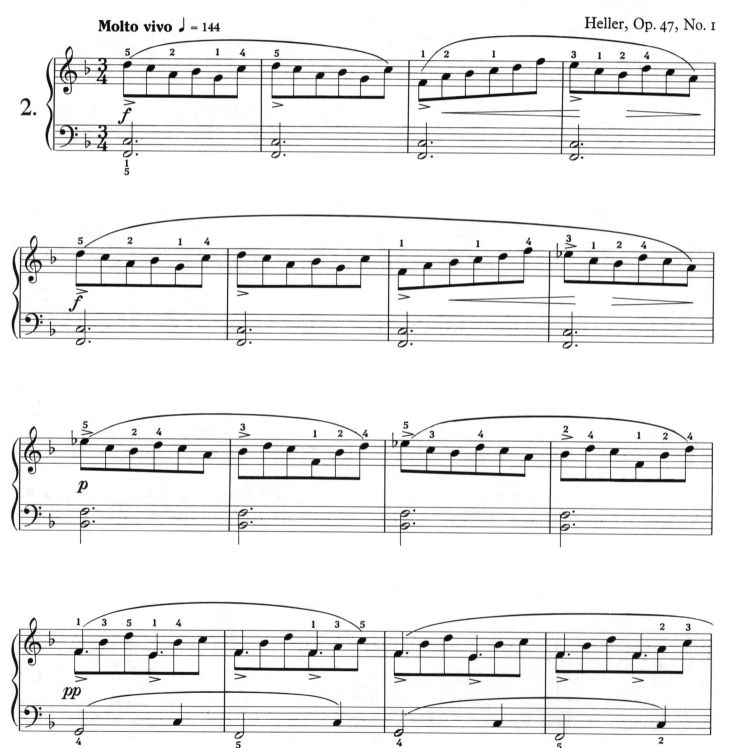

B. & Co. Ltd. 21990

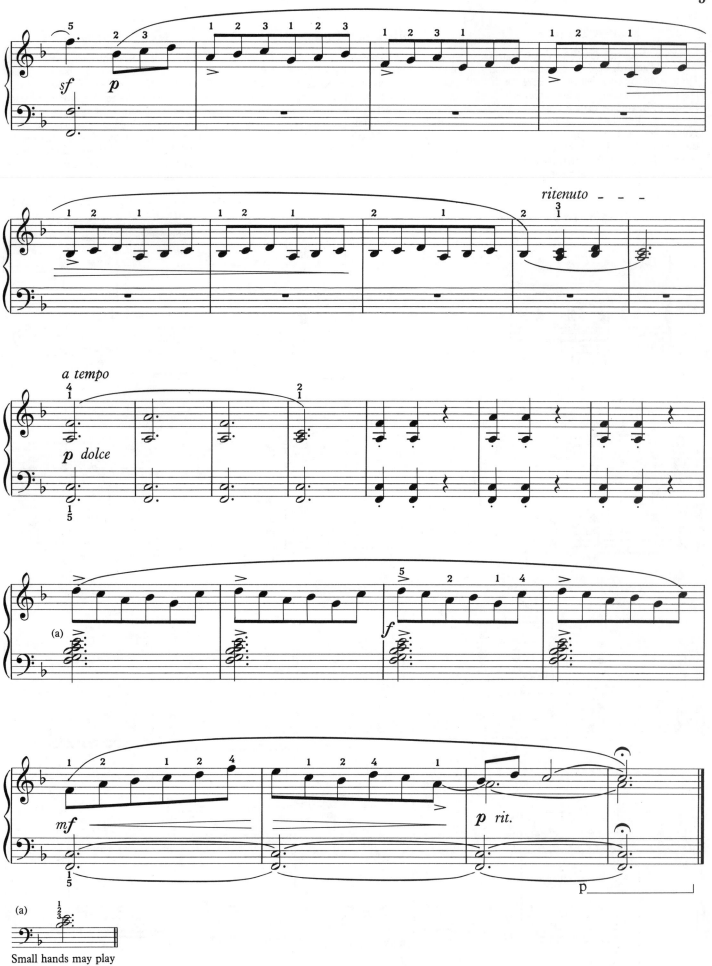

(a) Small hands may play

Gaiete et Tristesse

Assurez-vous que toutes les notes d'intervalles et d'accords donnent ensemble un son fondu. Observez les valeurs de durée et de sonorité des notes en opposition avec les parties mobiles, comme dans les mesures 5—6, 7—10, etc. Rendez bien la progression du rythme dans la suite des mesures et aux fins de phrases. Dans la section du milieu (Do mineur), faites chanter clairement la mélodie en opposition avec les accords brisés de la main gauche.

Mirth and Sadness

Ensure that all notes of intervals and chords sound dead together. Attend to time and tone values of notes against moving parts, as in bars 5—6, 7—10, etc. Make good rhythmical progression to each next bar and to the phrase endings. In the middle (C minor) section, let the melody sing clearly against L.H. broken chords.

Freude und Trauer

Achte beim Spielen der Akkorde auf exaktes, gleichzeitiges Anschlagen aller Töne. Tempo und Notenwerte sind in den Takten, wo einzelne Töne länger ausgehalten werden, genau zu beachten. Vergiss nicht den zum nächstfolgenden Takt und zum Ende einer Phrase hindrängenden Rhythmus. Im c-moll-Teil soll sich die Melodiestimme deutlich von den gebrochenen Akkorden der linken Hand abheben.

Beethoven
1770—1827

8

Polonaise en Sol mineur

Ce morceau doit être joué de façon plutôt solennelle et très rythmique. Observez tous les détails du *legato* et du *staccato*. Donnez aux notes de la basse une belle sonorité pour soutenir la ligne mélodique. Dans une Polonaise, la cadence tombe sur le second ou le troisième battement.

Polonaise in G Minor

This piece must be rather stately and very rhythmical. Attend to all details of *legato* and *staccato*. Give the bass notes nice sonorous tone to support the melodic line.

In a Polonaise, the cadential point falls on the second or third beat.

Polonaise in g-moll

Dieses Stück soll sehr feierlich und rhythmisch vorgetragen werden. Beachte genau jedes Legato und Staccato. Um die melodische Linie entsprechend zu unterstützen, müssen die Basstöne klangvoll gespielt werden.

In der Polonaise fällt die Schlussbildung (Tonika) immer auf den zweiten oder dritten Taktschlag.

Prelude.
Op. 65, no 2.

Il faut une sonorité chantante et douce et un mouvement tranquille. Assurez-vous que les notes longues ont une sonorité initiale suffisante pour leur permettre de donner leur pleine valeur au chant.

Prelude
Op. 65, No. 2

Sweet singing tone and tranquil movement are needed. Ensure that long notes have enough initial tone to enable them to sing for their full value.

Präludium

Eine singende Tongebung sowie ein ruhiges Tempo sind hier notwendig. Der Anschlag muss bei langen Noten so gestaltet werden, dass diese ihrem vollen Wert entsprechend hörbar sind.

Kirchner
1823—1903

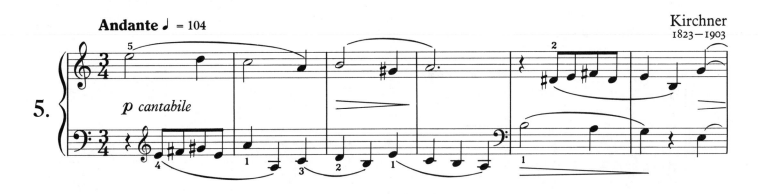

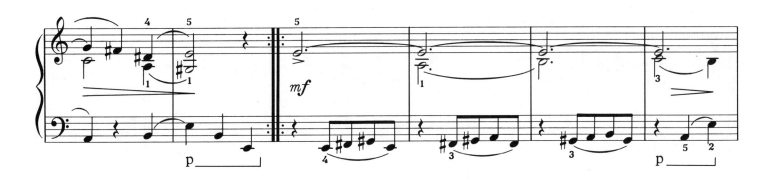

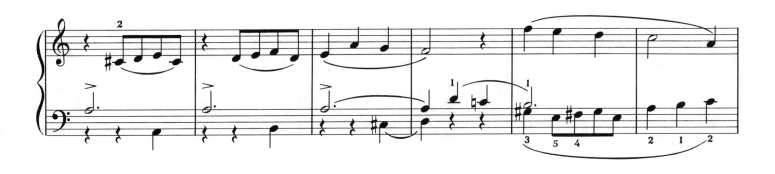

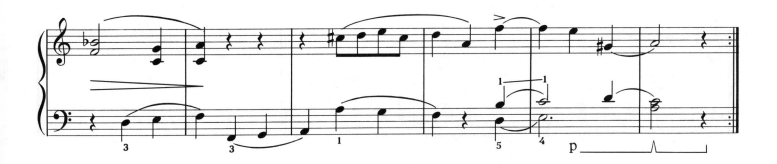

Chanson et Danse

Un air animé avec un chant allègre et joyeux. Rendez bien la progression rythmique de mesure en mesure et ayez soin de jouer les seconde et troisième notes aux mesures 2, 3, 4 et endroits similaires très légèrement. La seconde partie du morceau prend une sonorité plus chaude.

Song and Dance

A lively tune with joyous lilt. Make good rhythmical progression to each next bar and take care to play the second and third notes in bars 2, 3, 4, and similar places quite lightly. The second part of the piece takes a warmer tone.

Lied und Tanz

Wir haben es hier mit einer lebendigen Melodie mit fröhlicher Stimmung zu tun. Achte auf den zum jeweiligen nächsten Takt hinstrebenden Rhythmus und spiele die zweite und dritte Note in den Takten 2, 3, 4 sowie an ähnlichen Stellen sehr leicht. Der zweite Teil des Stücks soll inniger vorgetragen werden als der erste.

Köhler
1820–1886

Allegro
(extrait d'une petite Sonate)

Ceci nécessite un doigté léger, impeccable, et un mouvement rythmique précis. Remarquez que la mélodie se trouve parfois au sommet d'intervalles brisés, comme dans les mesures 9 à 16, et ces notes doivent chanter en opposition avec les doubles croches qui forment le fond. Les petites mains peuvent ne jouer que les notes inférieures des octaves (mesures 9—16). Le jeu doit être direct et gai.

Allegro
(from a small Sonata)

This needs a light, clean touch and precise rhythmic movement. Observe that the melody sometimes lies at the top of broken intervals, as in bars 9—16, and these notes should sing against the background semiquavers. Small hands may play only the lower notes of octaves—bars 13—16. The mood should be straightforward and happy.

Allegro

Zu diesem Stück sind ein leichter, sauberer Anschlag sowie ein präziser Rhythmus notwendig. Beachte die Melodieführung, die manchmal, wie in den Takten 9—16, in den oberen Noten der gebrochenen Intervalle liegt und sich gegen die begleitenden Sechzehntelnoten gut abheben muss. Spieler mit kleinen Händen brauchen in den Takten 9—16 nur die unteren Oktavtöne zu spielen. Der Charakter dieses Stücks soll aufrichtig und beschwingt sein.

Haydn
1732—1809

12

Choral
(Aria)

Ce morceau doit avoir une bonne sonorité chantante et un mouvement rythmique tranquille. Observez que toutes les phrases commencent au quatrième battement et progressent régulièrement vers la mesure suivante.

Chorale
(Aria)
from *Anna Magdalena Bach Book*

This piece needs good singing tone and tranquil rhythmical movement. Observe that all the phrases begin on the fourth beat and make smooth progression to the next bar.

Choral
(aus dem Notenbüchlein
für Anna Magdalena Bach)

Singende Tongebung und eine ruhige Bewegung erfordert dieser Choral. Achte darauf, dass alle Phrasen im Auftakt beginnen und leicht zum jeweiligen nächsten Takt hindrängen.

Bach

Air
(extrait de la Sonate en Do)

Veillez à ce que ce morceau ait une belle qualité de sonorité chantante jusqu'au bout, en prenant soin des phrasés et des nuances. Prenez garde à une bonne entrée en jeu de la main gauche après les pauses.

Air
(from Sonata in C)

See that this is given a beautiful singing tone quality throughout, with care in phrasing and tone shading. Attend to correct entry of left hand after rests.

Air
(aus der Sonate C-dur)

Ein schöner, singender Ton unter Berücksichtigung der angegebenen Phrasierungen und Dynamik ist bei diesem Stück erforderlich. Achte nach Pausen auf den exakten Einsatz der linken Hand.

Haydn

14

Menuet et Trio
(extrait de la Sonate en Do)

Ce morceau nécessite un travail des doigts net. Il faut donner une bonne vitalité rythmique sans frapper avec une insistance exagérée. Observez que toutes les phrases commencent au troisième battement d'une mesure et progressent régulièrement vers la mesure suivante. La basse est importante dans la formation du rythme et d'un fond harmonique chaud pour la mélodie. Jouez-la seule et observez comment elle mène l'oreille à des points d'intérêt et de repos. Le *trio* est d'une sonorité un peu plus légère.

Minuet and Trio
(from Sonata in C)

This piece needs clean fingerwork. Good rhythmic vitality must be given without undue stressing of beats. Observe that all the phrases begin on the third beat of a bar and make smooth progression to the next bar. The bass is important in shaping the rhythm and making a warm harmonic background for the melody. Practise it alone and observe how it leads the ear to points of interest and repose. The *trio* is somewhat lighter in tone amount.

Menuett und Trio
(aus der Sonate C-dur)

Dieses Stück erfordert saubere Fingerarbeit und muss rhythmisch vital gespielt werden, jedoch ohne dass dabei einzelne Taktschläge übermässig betont werden. Beachte, dass alle Phrasen auftaktig beginnen und zum folgenden Takt hindrängen. Der Bass bestimmt hier den Rhythmus und formt den harmonischen Untergrund für die Melodie. Übe die Bass-Stimme allein und beobachte, wie sie das Ohr zu den Höhepunkten oder auch Ruhepunkten des Stücks führt. Das Trio ist in der Tonstärke etwas zurückzunehmen.

Menuetto   D.C.

B. & Co. Ltd. 21990

16

Ah ! Vous dirai - je Maman

Mozart a écrit une série de variations sur cet air français favori de nourrice. Ici nous avons le thème simple et la seconde variation, qui reproduit clairement le thème. En jouant cette variation, observez la durée exacte des notes comprises dans le demi-battement, et veillez à ce que les rythmes des mains droite et gauche se combinent pour former un groupe égal de quatre croches.

Ah! Vous dirai-je Maman

Mozart wrote a set of variations on this favourite French nursery tune. Here we have the simple theme and the second variation, which clearly carries the tune. In playing this variation, attend to exact timing of notes which enter on the half-beat, and see that the right and left-hand rhythms combine to make an equal four-quaver pattern.

Ah! Vous dirai-je Maman

Über dieses beliebte französische Kinderlied schrieb Mozart eine Reihe von Variationen, wovon wir hier das einfache Thema und die zweite Variation, in welcher das Thema klar zu erkennen ist, vorliegen haben. Beim Spielen dieser Variation muss der genaue Rhythmus bei den auf "und" kommenden Achtelnoten eingehalten werden. Achte darauf, dass sich die Noten der rechten und linken Hand zu einer gleichmässigen Vierachtelbewegung ergänzen.

Mozart
1756—1791

VARIATION 2

Largo

Il faut une sonorité pleine et chaleureuse avec, dans son ensemble, des graduations délicates qui doivent aller avec les contours mélodiques. Faites ressortir la mélodie qui se trouve au sommet des intervalles et des accords et, en même temps, tenez compte des valeurs de durée et de sonorité dans les parties internes aux deux mains.

Largo

Warmly sonorous tone is needed with delicate gradations in the amount of it to fit the melodic contours. Bring out the melody which lies at the top of intervals and chords and, at the same time, attend to time and tone values of inner parts in both hands.

Largo

Hier wird ein warmer, klangvoller Ton mit fein abgestufter Dynamik benötigt, der sich den melodischen Umrissen des Stücks gut anpasst. Hebe die über den Intervallen und Akkorden liegende Melodie klar hervor, ohne die Zeit- und Tonwerte der Mittelstimmen dabei ausser acht zu lassen.

Händel
Arr.: D.B.

19

B. & Co. Ltd. 21990

Étude en sol
L'hirondelle

Tout d'abord, sans jouer, exercez-vous au mouvement flottant du bras gauche. Etudiez les accords dont sont composés les groupes de doubles croches et formez bien la main à posséder les touches. Veillez à ce que la main droite intervienne exactement sur le battement de la noire, afin que la combinaison des parties forme des groupes égaux de doubles croches.

Study in G
The Swallow

At first, without playing, practise the left arm floating movement. Study the chords of which the semiquaver groups are built and shape the hand neatly to take hold of the keys. See that the right hand enters exactly on the quarter beat, so that equal groups of semiquavers are formed by the combined parts.

Etüde in G-dur
Die Schwalbe

Übe zuerst ohne zu spielen die wogende Bewegung des linken Armes und studiere anschliessend die Akkorde, aus denen sich die Sechzehntelfiguren zusammensetzen. Achte darauf, dass die Hand die genaue Stellung über den anzuschlagenden Tasten einnimmt. Der Einsatz der rechten Hand muss so akkurat erfolgen, dass die von beiden Händen zusammen gespielten Sechzehntelfiguren vollkommen gleichmässig erklingen.

Burgmüller

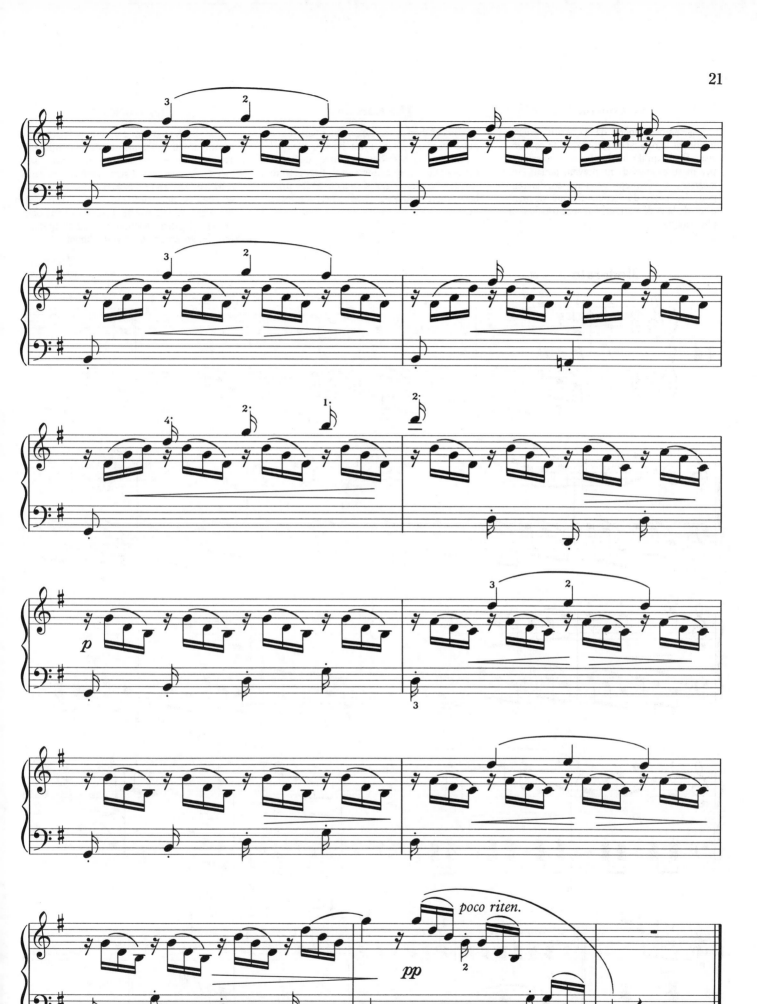

Le Coucou

L'accompagnement de la main gauche maintient la regularité rythmique de ce morceau. Il faut qu'il y ait deux accents métriques par mesure, mais ils ne doivent jamais être *marteles*, ils forment un fond murmurant pour les notes du "coucou" qui viennent d'ici, de là et de partout, qui sont proches ou plus éloignées.

The Cuckoo

The left-hand accompaniment keeps the pulse beating. There must be two metrical accents to the bar, but they must never be *bumped*; they form a murmurous background for the "cuckoo" notes, which come from here, there and everywhere, near or more distant.

Der Kuckuck

Die Begleitfiguren der linken Hand bestimmen den gleichmässigen Rhythmus des Stückes, wobei jeweils das erste und das vierte Sechzehntel einen *leichten* Akzent erhalten. Die ein Rauschen imitierende Begleitung ist der Hintergrund, von dem sich der Kuckucksruf (rechte Hand), der aus den verschiedensten Richtungen und Entfernungen zu kommen scheint, abhebt.

Hummel
1778—1837

24

Andantino

On constatera que l'accompagnement de la main gauche se compose d'harmonies brisées, dont on doit conserver le moelleux et la durée très égale, en faisant chanter doucement la mélodie par dessus. Aux mesures 9 à 12 l'avant-bras devrait être libre pour aider le cinquième doigt de la main à mettre l'air en relief.

Andantino

It will be found that the left-hand accompaniment is made up of broken harmonies. Keep these smooth and very evenly timed and let the melody sing sweetly above. In bars 9 to 12 the forearm should be free to help the fifth-finger side of the hand to bring out the tune.

Andantino

Spiele die aus gebrochenen Intervallen bestehende Begleitstimme der linken Hand zart und sehr gleichmässig und lasse die darüberliegende Melodiestimme mit einer süssen singenden Tongebung erklingen. Der Unterarm muss in den Takten 9—12 völlig entspannt sein, um die die Melodie spielende 5.-Finger-Seite der Hand unterstützen zu können.

B. & Co. Ltd. 21990

Processed and printed by
Halstan & Co. Ltd., Amersham, Bucks., England

5/04 (51348)